£10.95

GuestSpot

CHRISTMAS HITS
Playalong *for* Violin

WISE PUBLICATIONS
London/New York/Paris/Sydney/Copenhagen/Madrid/Tokyo

Exclusive Distributors:
Music Sales Limited
8/9 Frith Street, London W1V 5TZ, England.
Music Sales Pty Limited
120 Rothschild Avenue, Rosebery, NSW 2018, Australia.

Order No. AM966977
ISBN 0-7119-8439-5
This book © Copyright 2000 by Wise Publications.

Music arranged by Paul Honey.
Music processed by Enigma Music Production Services.
Cover photography by George Taylor.
Printed in the United Kingdom by Page Bros., Norwich, Norfolk.

CD produced by Paul Honey.
Instrumental solos by Dermot Crehan.
Engineered by Kester Sims.

Your Guarantee of Quality:
As publishers, we strive to produce every book to
the highest commercial standards.
The music has been freshly engraved and the book has been
carefully designed to minimise awkward page turns and
to make playing from it a real pleasure.
Particular care has been given to specifying acid-free, neutral-sized
paper made from pulps which have not been elemental chlorine bleached.
This pulp is from farmed sustainable forests and was
produced with special regard for the environment.
Throughout, the printing and binding have been planned to
ensure a sturdy, attractive publication which should give years of enjoyment.
If your copy fails to meet our high standards,
please inform us and we will gladly replace it.

Music Sales' complete catalogue describes thousands of
titles and is available in full colour sections by subject,
direct from Music Sales Limited.
Please state your areas of interest and send a
cheque/postal order for £1.50 for postage to:
Music Sales Limited, Newmarket Road, Bury St. Edmunds, Suffolk IP33 3YB.

www.musicsales.com

Fairytale Of New York

Words & Music by Shane MacGowan & Jem Finer

Happy Xmas (War Is Over)

Words & Music by John Lennon & Yoko Ono

9

I Believe In Father Christmas

Words & Music by Peter Sinfield & Greg Lake

Moderately

I Wish It Could Be Christmas Every Day

Words & Music by Roy Wood

Moderately (Swung ♪s)

molto rall.

Lonely This Christmas

Words & Music by Mike Chapman & Nicky Chinn

Step into the spotlight with...

GUEST SPOT

...and playalong *with* the specially recorded backing tracks

A great book and CD series,
each title available in arrangements for
**FLUTE, CLARINET, ALTO SAXOPHONE,
TENOR SAXOPHONE*, TRUMPET* and VIOLIN***

Pull Out

Now you can own professional

when you play all thes

for Clarinet, Flute, Alto Saxophon

The *essential* book & CD series...

From Jazz, Blues and Swing to Ballads,
Showstoppers, Film and TV Themes, here
are all your favourite Chart Hits and more!
Check out the special editions featuring legends
of pop, **Abba** and **The Beatles**.

The Music Book...

Top line arrangements for 10 songs,
plus a fingering guide for wind instruments.

The CD...

Hear full performance versions of all the songs.
Then play along with the recorded accompaniments.

ABBA
Includes:
Dancing Queen
Fernando
Mamma Mia
Waterloo

AM960905 Clarinet
AM960894 Flute
AM960916 Alto Saxophone
AM960927 Violin

BALLADS
Includes:
Candle In The Wind
Imagine
Killing Me Softly With His Song
Wonderful Tonight

AM941787 Clarinet
AM941798 Flute
AM941809 Alto Saxophone

THE BEATLES
Includes:
All You Need Is Love
Hey Jude
Lady Madonna
Yesterday

NO90682 Clarinet
NO90683 Flute
NO90684 Alto Saxophone

CHRISTMAS
Includes:
Frosty The Snowman
*Have Yourself A Merry Little
    Christmas*
Mary's Boy Child
Winter Wonderland

AM950400 Clarinet
AM950411 Flute
AM950422 Alto Saxophone

have your very
backing band...

reat melody line arrangements
enor Saxophone*, Trumpet* and Violin*

FILM THEMES
Playalong *for* Clarinet

NINETIES HITS
Playalong *for* Saxophone

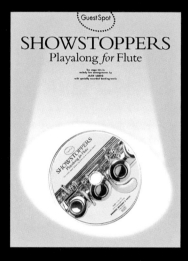

SHOWSTOPPERS
Playalong *for* Flute

SWING
Playalong *for* Trumpet

LASSIC BLUES

cludes:
ver
arlem Nocturne
oonglow
und Midnight

M941743 Clarinet
M941754 Flute
M941765 Alto Saxophone

LASSICS

cludes:
r On The 'G' String - Bach
piter (from The Planets Suite) -
Holst
de To Joy (Theme from
Symphony No.9 'Choral') -
Beethoven
van Lake (Theme) -
Tchaikovsky.

M955537 Clarinet
M955548 Flute
M955560 Violin

FILM THEMES

Includes:
Circle Of Life (The Lion King)
Love Is All Around
(Four Weddings & A Funeral)
Moon River
(Breakfast At Tiffany's)
You Must Love Me (Evita)

AM941864 Clarinet
AM941875 Flute
AM941886 Alto Saxophone

JAZZ

Includes:
Fly Me To The Moon
Opus One
Satin Doll
Straight No Chaser

AM941700 Clarinet
AM941710 Flute
AM941721 Alto Saxophone

NINETIES HITS

Includes:
Falling Into You (Celine Dion)
Never Ever (All Saints)
Tears In Heaven (Eric Clapton)
2 Become 1 (Spice Girls)

AM952853 Clarinet
AM952864 Flute
AM952875 Alto Saxophone

No.1 HITS

Includes:
A Whiter Shade Of Pale
(Procol Harum)
Every Breath You Take
(The Police)
No Matter What (Boyzone)
Unchained Melody
(The Righteous Brothers).

AM955603 Clarinet
AM955614 Flute
AM955625 Alto Saxophone
AM959530 Violin

SHOWSTOPPERS

Includes:
Big Spender (Sweet Charity)
Bring Him Home (Les Misérables)
I Know Him So Well (Chess)
Somewhere (West Side Story)

AM941820 Clarinet
AM941831 Flute
AM941842 Alto Saxophone

SWING

Includes:
I'm Getting Sentimental
Over You
Is You Is Or Is You Ain't
My Baby?
Perdido
Tuxedo Junction

AM949377 Clarinet
AM960575 Trumpet
AM949399 Alto Saxophone
AM959618 Tenor Saxophone

TV THEMES

Includes:
Black Adder
Home And Away
London's Burning
Star Trek

AM941908 Clarinet
AM941919 Flute
AM941920 Alto Saxophone

* Selected titles only

Sample the *whole* series of *Guest Spot* with these special double CD bumper compilations...

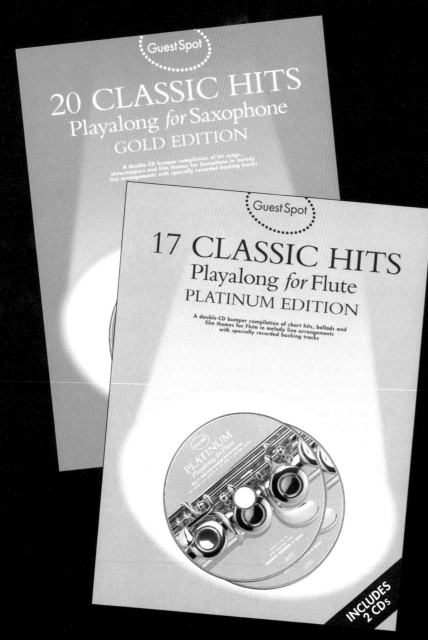

PUB04626

Mistletoe And Wine

Words by Leslie Stewart & Jeremy Paul
Music by Keith Strachan

Moderately

Merry Xmas Everybody

Words & Music by Neville Holder & James Lea

poco rall.

Stop The Cavalry

Words & Music by Jona Lewie

25

Wonderful Christmastime

Words & Music by Paul McCartney

28

A Spaceman Came Travelling

Words & Music by Chris De Burgh

Moderately